Macmillan/McGraw-Hill

S0-BAI-027

Vocabulary Power

Social Studies • Grade 4

Teacher's Note

This component provides Vocabulary Power Activities to help students preview, review, and retain new vocabulary. The Vocabulary Card section contains every highlighted term in the pupil edition. Use these cards as a tool to review vocabulary or in conjunction with the Vocabulary Power Activities. There is also a Vocabulary Review section that contains vocabulary activities for every chapter in the pupil's edition. Answers to the Practice pages are in the back of this book.

Macmillan/McGraw-Hill

A Division of The McGraw-Hill Companies

Published by Macmillan/McGraw-Hill, of McGraw-Hill Education, a division of The McGraw-Hill Companies, Inc.,
Two Penn Plaza, New York, NY 10121

Printed in the United States of America

2 3 4 5 6 7 8 9 047 09 08 07 06 05 04 03 02

Contents

Word Association Chart

A word association chart allows you to elicit students' prior knowledge of the lesson vocabulary. Once the lesson material has been covered, you can return to the chart to record what students have learned about the vocabulary words. A blank word association chart appears on page 67.

Follow these steps to create a word association chart:

1. Draw the chart below on a transparency or on the board.

Vocabulary	Related Words and Phrases	
	Before Reading	After Reading

2. Ask students to think about what they know about each vocabulary word or phrase. Ask them what words and phrases come to mind when they think of each term. Write their responses in the chart in the "Before Reading" column.

3. Review the completed "Before Reading" column and record the information on a sheet of paper if necessary.

4. After reading the lesson, display the transparency or redraw the chart on the board, including the information in the "Before Reading" column.

5. Again ask students to talk about what words and phrases come to mind when they think of each vocabulary word, this time using the knowledge they gained from the lesson.

Alternative activity: Create a blackline master of the word association chart including the lesson vocabulary. Distribute copies to students. Have students work on the chart individually or in pairs.

Word Sort

Word sorts enable students to identify the common features of multiple vocabulary words. A word sort involves providing students with a list of vocabulary words and having them sort them into two or more categories. A blank word sort chart appears on page 68.

Follow these steps to complete a word sort:

1. Examine the lesson vocabulary list to determine into what categories the vocabulary words can be divided. You may not be able to place all words in a given vocabulary list in related categories.

2. Write the list of vocabulary words on the board.

3. Next to the vocabulary list, make a table for the word sort categories. Write the name of each category at the top of each column. See the example below.

Geography

compass rose	map key
continent	ocean
hemisphere	physical map
landform map	scale

Features of Earth	Features of Maps	Types of Maps
continent	compass rose	landform map
hemisphere	map key	physical map
ocean	scale	

Pre-teaching option: You may want to use a word sort to pre-teach lesson vocabulary.

Word Map

A word map is a graphic representation of the meaning of a vocabulary word. It illustrates the general class to which the word belongs, characteristics or properties of the word, and examples. It answers the questions:

1. What is it?

2. What is it like?

3. What are some examples?

See the word map for *ocean* below.

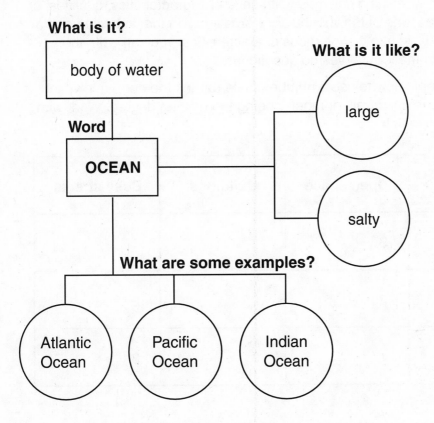

Follow these steps to create a word map:

1. Draw the word map for *ocean* on the board. Introduce the map to students as a picture of what they need to know to understand a new word. Explain that the word being defined is in the main box, and the clusters surrounding the main box answer the three questions above. Help students verbalize a definition of *ocean* using the words shown in the chart.

2. Have the students practice making a word map for another word, such as *continent.* Help students verbalize a definition of the word using the clustered descriptives.

3. Choose a vocabulary word from the lesson that is appropriate for the word map format, particularly a noun or an action verb. Have students work individually or in pairs to make a word map for the assigned word.

Word Comparison Chart

Word comparison charts enable students to see the similarities and differences between related words to help them understand the uniqueness of each word. They can be used to help students prepare for vocabulary assessment, such as a basic attributes quiz.

Follow these steps to create a word comparison chart:

1. Make a chart similar to the sample below. In the first column make a list of vocabulary words that share some common feature.

2. At the top of the remaining columns write several characteristics, qualities, or abilities of at least one of the vocabulary words listed in the first column. If a given vocabulary list has dichotomous characteristics, you can write the column heads in the form of yes/no questions.

3. Explain to students how to use a number scale to rank the degree to which an item has a particular trait, number 1 being the highest degree. Work with students to fill in the chart.

Vocabulary	Open space	Buildings	Busy streets
urban area	3	1	1
suburb	2	2	2
rural area	1	3	3

Pre-teaching option: You may want to use a word comparison chart at the beginning of a lesson to pre-teach the lesson vocabulary.

Word Clues

Word clues, or riddles, can help students to acquire vocabulary in a fun and creative way. You can introduce students to this method of studying vocabulary by first writing word clues yourself and asking students to solve them.

Below is a sample set of vocabulary and corresponding word clues. Use these as a guide to help you write word clues for the lesson vocabulary your class is studying.

island	river
hill	season
lake	geography

1. I am the study of Earth and all the things that live on Earth. What am I?
2. I am a stream of water that flows into an ocean or lake. What am I?
3. I am land surrounded by water. What am I?
4. I am land that is higher than the land around it. What am I?
5. I am spring, summer, fall, or winter. What am I?
6. I am a body of water surrounded by land. What am I?

Extension: Once students are familiar with word clues, you may have them write their own clues for the lesson vocabulary.

Word Links

Word links help students to understand and communicate the relationship between a vocabulary term and the broader theme of the lesson within which that term is found. A blank word links chart appears on page 69.

Follow these steps to develop a word links chart:

1. On a transparency or the board, write the lesson title, or another term that conveys the theme of the lesson.

2. Draw a two-column chart on the board. Title the first column "Vocabulary." The title of the second column should be "Links to [insert the unit title or theme]."

3. Review the definitions of the vocabulary terms with students.

4. Have students work as a class to determine how each term is related to the title or theme of the lesson. Decide together on one sentence that communicates this relationship. Write the sentence in the second column.

Extension: Once you've completed the word links chart, review the sentences in the second column with the class. Look for and discuss any "links" among the vocabulary words themselves.

Vocabulary Power Word Cards

The following section contains every highlighted term in the pupil edition. The words are in the order in which they appear in the text. These pages may be copied and used to make word cards with definitions written on the back, as a tool for second-language learners, or in conjunction with the Vocabulary Power Activities in this book. Use the cards to help students preview and review vocabulary for each chapter or unit.

Economics	Citizenship
Social Studies Handbook	Social Studies Handbook
Culture	Science
Social Studies Handbook	Social Studies Handbook
Technology	Society
Social Studies Handbook	Social Studies Handbook
Geography	History
Social Studies Handbook	Social Studies Handbook
Government	Social Studies Skills
Social Studies Handbook	Social Studies Handbook
New York City	urban
Reading Social Studies	Reading Social Studies

rural Reading Social Studies	**visuals** Reading Social Studies
context clues Reading Social Studies	**immigrants** Reading Social Studies
boycott Reading Social Studies	**oceans** Reviewing Geography Skills
continents Reviewing Geography Skills	**hemisphere** Reviewing Geography Skills
equator Reviewing Geography Skills	**cardinal directions** Reviewing Geography Skills
compass rose Reviewing Geography Skills	**intermediate directions** Reviewing Geography Skills

relative location	map symbol
Reviewing Geography Skills	Reviewing Geography Skills
map key	scale
Reviewing Geography Skills	Reviewing Geography Skills
locator	political map
Reviewing Geography Skills	Reviewing Geography Skills
physical maps	landform maps
Reviewing Geography Skills	Reviewing Geography Skills
transportation map	historical map
Reviewing Geography Skills	Reviewing Geography Skills
Western Hemisphere	geography
Introduction	Introduction

landforms *Introduction*	plain *Introduction*
tundra *Introduction*	Rocky Mountains *Introduction*
Canada *Introduction*	Mexico *Introduction*
Amazon Rain Forest *Introduction*	Andes Mountains *Introduction*
Everglades *Introduction*	wetlands *Introduction*
Coastal Plain *Introduction*	Interior Plains *Introduction*

Columbia Plateau *Introduction*	elevation *Introduction*
climate *Introduction*	temperature *Introduction*
precipitation *Introduction*	environment *Introduction*
natural resources *Introduction*	renewable *Introduction*
nonrenewable *Introduction*	minerals *Introduction*
fuels *Introduction*	pollution *Introduction*

conservation	immigrants
Introduction	*Introduction*
slavery	ancestors
Introduction	*Introduction*
population	cultures
Introduction	*Introduction*
customs	heritage
Introduction	*Introduction*
ethnic group	government
Introduction	*Introduction*
Constitution	democratic republic
Introduction	*Introduction*

citizens *Introduction*	taxes *Introduction*
Washington, D.C. *Introduction*	Congress *Introduction*
President *Introduction*	United States Supreme Court *Introduction*
checks and balances *Introduction*	outline *Introduction*
economy *Introduction*	services *Introduction*
free-enterprise system *Introduction*	entrepreneurs *Introduction*

profit	investors
Introduction	Introduction
consumers	regions
Introduction	Introduction
interdependent	transportation
Introduction	Introduction
Rio Grande	Gulf of Mexico
Chapter 1, Lesson 1	Chapter 1, Lesson 1
Colorado Plateau	canyons
Chapter 1, Lesson 1	Chapter 1, Lesson 1
Grand Canyon	mesa
Chapter 1, Lesson 1	Chapter 1, Lesson 1

buttes Chapter 1, Lesson 1	# Colorado River Chapter 1, Lesson 1
erosion Chapter 1, Lesson 1	## Painted Desert Chapter 1, Lesson 2
deserts Chapter 1, Lesson 2	## Sonoran Desert Chapter 1, Lesson 2
adapt Chapter 1, Lesson 2	**drought** Chapter 1, Lesson 2
petroleum Chapter 1, Lesson 2	**latitude** Chapter 1, Geography Skills
parallels Chapter 1, Geography Skills	**degrees** Chapter 1, Geography Skills

longitude	prime meridian
Chapter 1, Geography Skills	Chapter 1, Geography Skills
meridians	global grid
Chapter 1, Geography Skills	Chapter 1, Geography Skills
aquifers	spring
Chapter 1, Lesson 3	Chapter 1, Lesson 3
aqueduct	dry farming
Chapter 1, Lesson 3	Chapter 1, Lesson 3
Beaumont, Texas	crude oil
Chapter 1, Lesson 3	Chapter 1, Lesson 3
refinery	petrochemicals
Chapter 1, Lesson 3	Chapter 1, Lesson 3

pueblo Chapter 2, Lesson 1	adobe Chapter 2, Lesson 1
reservations Chapter 2, Lesson 1	Old Oraibi Chapter 2, Lesson 1
Gobi Desert Chapter 2, Lesson 2	Mongolia Chapter 2, Lesson 2
steppe Chapter 2, Lesson 2	nomadic Chapter 2, Lesson 2
cashmere Chapter 2, Lesson 2	Ulaanbaatar Chapter 2, Lesson 2
Christopher Columbus Chapter 2, Lesson 3	Francisco Coronado Chapter 2, Lesson 3

conquistador *Chapter 2, Lesson 3*	missions *Chapter 2, Lesson 3*
Eusebio Francisco Kino *Chapter 2, Lesson 3*	ranchos *Chapter 2, Lesson 3*
San Xavier del Bac *Chapter 2, Lesson 3*	Tucson *Chapter 2, Lesson 3*
Santa Fe, New Mexico *Chapter 2, Lesson 3*	The Alamo *Chapter 2, Lesson 3*
Davy Crockett *Chapter 2, Lesson 3*	time line *Chapter 2, Study Skills*
vaqueros *Chapter 2, Lesson 4*	Nat Love *Chapter 2, Lesson 4*

cattle drive	Chisholm Trail
Chapter 2, Lesson 4	Chapter 2, Lesson 4

San Antonio, Texas	Abilene, Kansas
Chapter 2, Lesson 4	Chapter 2, Lesson 4

Lizzie Johnson Williams	barbed wire
Chapter 2, Lesson 4	Chapter 2, Lesson 4

consequence	evaluate
Chapter 2, Skills	Chapter 2, Skills

industry	high technology
Chapter 2, Lesson 5	Chapter 2, Lesson 5

astronomers	Kitt Peak
Chapter 2, Lesson 5	Chapter 2, Lesson 5

NAFTA Chapter 2, Lesson 5	**Phoenix, Arizona** Chapter 2, Lesson 5
Mississippi River Chapter 3, Lesson 1	**source** Chapter 3, Lesson 1
tributaries Chapter 3, Lesson 1	**river basin** Chapter 3, Lesson 1
mouth Chapter 3, Lesson 1	**port** Chapter 3, Lesson 1
Okefenokee Swamp Chapter 3, Lesson 1	**delta** Chapter 3, Lesson 1
map scale Chapter 3, Geography Skills Lesson	**small-scale map** Chapter 3, Geography Skills Lesson

large-scale map	agriculture
Chapter 3, Geography Skills Lesson	Chapter 3, Lesson 2
growing season	cash crops
Chapter 3, Lesson 2	Chapter 3, Lesson 2
irrigation	tourists
Chapter 3, Lesson 2	Chapter 3, Lesson 2
coal	labor union
Chapter 3, Lesson 3	Chapter 3, Lesson 3
council	Echota
Chapter 4, Lesson 1	Chapter 4, Lesson 1
Sequoyah	syllabary
Chapter 4, Lesson 1	Chapter 4, Lesson 1

Trail of Tears Chapter 4, Lesson 1	Tahlequah, Oklahoma Chapter 4, Lesson 1
Jamestown, Virginia Chapter 4, Lesson 2	colony Chapter 4, Lesson 2
Williamsburg Chapter 4, Lesson 2	Chesapeake Bay Chapter 4, Lesson 2
Thomas Jefferson Chapter 4, Lesson 2	House of Burgesses Chapter 4, Lesson 2
Declaration of Independence Chapter 4, Lesson 2	endowed Chapter 4, Lesson 2
unalienable Chapter 4, Lesson 2	instituted Chapter 4, Lesson 2

deriving Chapter 4, Lesson 2	**consent** Chapter 4, Lesson 2
Nelson Mandela Chapter 4, Lesson 3	**South Africa** Chapter 4, Lesson 3
Cape Town Chapter 4, Lesson 3	**apartheid** Chapter 4, Lesson 3
townships Chapter 4, Lesson 3	**Frederik Willem de Klerk** Chapter 4, Lesson 3
decision Chapter 4, Skills	**plantations** Chapter 4, Lesson 4
Frederick Douglass Chapter 4, Lesson 4	**Harriet Tubman** Chapter 4, Lesson 4

Underground Railroad Chapter 4, Lesson 4	abolition Chapter 4, Lesson 4
Union Chapter 4, Lesson 4	Abraham Lincoln Chapter 4, Lesson 4
Confederacy Chapter 4, Lesson 4	Jefferson Davis Chapter 4, Lesson 4
Civil War Chapter 4, Lesson 4	Robert E. Lee Chapter 4, Lesson 4
Emancipation Proclamation Chapter 4, Lesson 4	Ulysses S. Grant Chapter 4, Lesson 4
summary Chapter 4, Study Skills	segregation Chapter 4, Lesson 5

Atlanta, Georgia Chapter 4, Lesson 5	Montgomery, Alabama Chapter 4, Lesson 5
civil rights Chapter 4, Lesson 5	Martin Luther King, Jr. Chapter 4, Lesson 5
Rosa Parks Chapter 4, Lesson 5	boycott Chapter 4, Lesson 5
Condoleezza Rice Chapter 4, Lesson 5	Birmingham, Alabama Chapter 4, Lesson 5
harbor Chapter 5, Lesson 1	Atlantic Coastal Plain Chapter 5, Lesson 1
bays Chapter 5, Lesson 1	Delaware Bay Chapter 5, Lesson 1

Appalachian Mountains Chapter 5, Lesson 1	**glaciers** Chapter 5, Lesson 1
Appalachian Trail Chapter 5, Lesson 1	**fall line** Chapter 5, Lesson 1
broadleaf Chapter 5, Lesson 1	**needleleaf** Chapter 5, Lesson 1
repose Chapter 5, Lesson 1	**blindsided** Chapter 5, Lesson 2
demolished Chapter 5, Lesson 2	**devoured** Chapter 5, Lesson 2
hands Chapter 5, Lesson 2	**foliage** Chapter 5, Lesson 2

granite	quarries
Chapter 5, Lesson 2	Chapter 5, Lesson 2
cause	effect
Chapter 5, Skills	Chapter 5, Skills
Baltimore, Maryland	Great Lakes
Chapter 5, Lesson 3	Chapter 5, Lesson 3
canals	locks
Chapter 5, Lesson 3	Chapter 5, Lesson 3
Buffalo, New York	Montréal, Quebec
Chapter 5, Lesson 3	Chapter 5, Lesson 3
suburbs	urban
Chapter 5, Lesson 3	Chapter 5, Lesson 3

metropolitan area Chapter 5, Lesson 3	commute Chapter 5, Lesson 3
Deganawida Chapter 6, Lesson 1	Hiawatha Chapter 6, Lesson 1
Iroquois Confederacy Chapter 6, Lesson 1	longhouses Chapter 6, Lesson 1
clans Chapter 6, Lesson 1	Great Law of Peace Chapter 6, Lesson 1
sachems Chapter 6, Lesson 1	Onondaga Chapter 6, Lesson 1
imported Chapter 6, Lesson 2	exported Chapter 6, Lesson 2

Patriots

Crispus Attucks

Boston Massacre

John Adams

Boston Tea Party

Minutemen

Paul Revere

William Dawes

Lexington

American Revolution

George Washington

inference

Industrial Revolution Chapter 6, Lesson 3	**Samuel Slater** Chapter 6, Lesson 3
Hannah Wilkinson Slater Chapter 6, Lesson 3	**invention** Chapter 6, Lesson 3
Samuel Morse Chapter 6, Lesson 3	**telegraph** Chapter 6, Lesson 3
Ellis Island Chapter 6, Lesson 3	**tenements** Chapter 6, Lesson 3
sweatshops Chapter 6, Lesson 3	**India** Chapter 6, Lesson 4
Mumbai Chapter 6, Lesson 4	**Migrated** Chapter 6, Lesson 4

distribution map

megalopolis

Boswash

terrorism

George W. Bush

Central Plains

Great Plains

prairie

livestock

graph

circle graph

line graph

lake effect *Chapter 7, Lesson 2*	tornadoes *Chapter 7, Lesson 2*
blizzards *Chapter 7, Lesson 2*	Chicago, Illinois *Chapter 7, Lesson 2*
Green Bay, Wisconsin *Chapter 7, Lesson 2*	Mesabi Range *Chapter 7, Lesson 3*
Black Hills *Chapter 7, Lesson 3*	Mount Rushmore National Memorial *Chapter 7, Lesson 3*
Gutzon Borglum *Chapter 7, Lesson 3*	Calvin Coolidge *Chapter 7, Lesson 3*
iron *Chapter 7, Lesson 3*	ore *Chapter 7, Lesson 3*

Duluth, Minnesota Chapter 7, Lesson 3	Detroit, Michigan Chapter 7, Lesson 3
open-pit mining Chapter 7, Lesson 3	taconite Chapter 7, Lesson 3
reclamation Chapter 7, Lesson 3	frontier Chapter 8, Lesson 1
Jean Baptiste Point du Sable Chapter 8, Lesson 1	pioneers Chapter 8, Lesson 1
flatboats Chapter 8, Lesson 1	Conestoga wagons Chapter 8, Lesson 1
sod Chapter 8, Lesson 1	John Deere Chapter 8, Lesson 1

generalization	teepees
Chapter 8, Thinking Skills	Chapter 8, Lesson 2
Sitting Bull	George Custer
Chapter 8, Lesson 2	Chapter 8, Lesson 2
Crazy Horse	Henry Ford
Chapter 8, Lesson 2	Chapter 8, Lesson 3
migration	mass production
Chapter 8, Lesson 3	Chapter 8, Lesson 3
assembly line	Amelia Earhart
Chapter 8, Lesson 3	Chapter 8, Lesson 3
robots	combine
Chapter 8, Lesson 3	Chapter 8, Lesson 4

agribusiness	food processing
Chapter 8, Lesson 4	Chapter 8, Lesson 4
specialize	subsistence farming
Chapter 8, Lesson 4	Chapter 8, Lesson 5
commercial farming	industrialization
Chapter 8, Lesson 5	Chapter 8, Lesson 5
Pike's Peak	Yellowstone National Park
Chapter 9, Lesson 1	Chapter 9, Lesson 1
geysers	Grand Teton National Park
Chapter 9, Lesson 1	Chapter 9, Lesson 1
Continental Divide	Mesa Verde
Chapter 9, Lesson 1	Chapter 9, Lesson 1

San Luis Valley Chapter 9, Lesson 2	**caverns** Chapter 9, Lesson 2
fancy Chapter 9, Lesson 2	**generates** Chapter 9, Lesson 2
homage Chapter 9, Lesson 2	**timberline** Chapter 9, Lesson 2
Great Salt Lake Chapter 9, Lesson 2	**vegetation map** Chapter 9, Geography Skills
smelting Chapter 9, Lesson 3	**slag** Chapter 9, Lesson 3
Salt Lake City, Utah Chapter 9, Lesson 3	**Chief Washakie** Chapter 10, Lesson 1

Wind River Valley	treaty
Chapter 10, Lesson 1	Chapter 10, Lesson 1
Fort Hall Reservation	Meriwether Lewis
Chapter 10, Lesson 1	Chapter 10, Lesson 2
William Clark	Louisiana Purchase
Chapter 10, Lesson 2	Chapter 10, Lesson 2
expedition	York
Chapter 10, Lesson 2	Chapter 10, Lesson 2
Sacagawea	Denver
Chapter 10, Lesson 2	Chapter 10, Lesson 2
Central City, Colorado	ghost town
Chapter 10, Lesson 2	Chapter 10, Lesson 2

transcontinental	Promontory Point
Chapter 10, Lesson 2	Chapter 10, Lesson 2
conclusion	suffrage
Chapter 10, Thinking Skills	Chapter 10, Lesson 3
Elizabeth Cady Stanton	Lucretia Mott
Chapter 10, Lesson 3	Chapter 10, Lesson 3
Susan B. Anthony	secure
Chapter 10, Lesson 3	Chapter 10, Lesson 3
mockery	Esther Morris
Chapter 10, Lesson 3	Chapter 10, Lesson 3
South Pass City	Jeannette Rankin
Chapter 10, Lesson 3	Chapter 10, Lesson 3

Nellie Tayloe Ross Chapter 10, Lesson 3	**reference source** Chapter 10, Study Skills
dictionary Chapter 10, Study Skills	**guide word** Chapter 10, Study Skills
encyclopedia Chapter 10, Study Skills	**CD-ROM** Chapter 10, Study Skills
Internet Chapter 10, Study Skills	**gorge** Chapter 10, Lesson 4
Sun Valley, Idaho Chapter 10, Lesson 4	**Vail, Colorado** Chapter 10, Lesson 4
Aspen, Colorado Chapter 10, Lesson 4	**Park City, Utah** Chapter 10, Lesson 4

Switzerland	Alps
Chapter 10, Lesson 5	Chapter 10, Lesson 4
landlocked	Jura Mountains
Chapter 10, Lesson 5	Chapter 10, Lesson 5
cantons	Mt. McKinley
Chapter 10, Lesson 5	Chapter 11, Lesson 1
Cascade Range	Sierra Nevada
Chapter 11, Lesson 1	Chapter 11, Lesson 1
Coast Ranges	Great Basin
Chapter 11, Lesson 1	Chapter 11, Lesson 1
earthquakes	volcano
Chapter 11, Lesson 1	Chapter 11, Lesson 1

lava Chapter 11, Lesson 1	**Hawaii** Chapter 11, Lesson 1
Mount St. Helens Chapter 11, Lesson 1	**road map** Chapter 11, Geography Skills
interstate highway Chapter 11, Geography Skills	**Death Valley** Chapter 11, Lesson 2
Mount Waialeale Chapter 11, Lesson 2	**rain forests** Chapter 11, Lesson 2
Olympic National Park Chapter 11, Lesson 2	**rain shadow** Chapter 11, Lesson 2
point of view Chapter 11, Thinking Skills	**fact** Chapter 11, Thinking Skills

opinion Chapter 11, Thinking Skills	editorial Chapter 11, Thinking Skills
Central Valley Chapter 11, Lesson 3	Central Valley Project Chapter 11, Lesson 3
fertilizers Chapter 11, Lesson 3	logging Chapter 11, Lesson 3
deforestation Chapter 11, Lesson 3	taro Chapter 12, Lesson 1
Kamehameha Chapter 12, Lesson 1	James Cook Chapter 12, Lesson 1
Lydia Liliuokalani Chapter 12, Lesson 1	James Marshall Chapter 12, Lesson 2

American River Chapter 12, Lesson 2	Gold Rush Chapter 12, Lesson 2
San Francisco Chapter 12, Lesson 2	Forty-Niners Chapter 12, Lesson 2
Jim Beckwourth Chapter 12, Lesson 2	mother lode Chapter 12, Lesson 2
Nome Chapter 12, Lesson 2	primary source Chapter 12, Study Skills
secondary source Chapter 12, Study Skills	Seattle Chapter 12, Lesson 3
César Chávez Chapter 12, Lesson 3	Dolores Huerta Chapter 12, Lesson 3

strike	discrimination
Chapter 12, Lesson 3	Chapter 12, Lesson 3

frame of reference	Hollywood
Chapter 12, Thinking Skills	Chapter 12, Lesson 4

silicon	software
Chapter 12, Lesson 4	Chapter 12, Lesson 4

Cupertino	Redmond
Chapter 12, Lesson 4	Chapter 12, Lesson 4

Silicon Valley	urban sprawl
Chapter 12, Lesson 4	Chapter 12, Lesson 4

Pacific Rim	Japan
Chapter 12, Lesson 5	Chapter 12, Lesson 5

Tokyo	Yokohama
Chapter 12, Lesson 5	Chapter 12, Lesson 5

Nagoya	Osaka
Chapter 12, Lesson 5	Chapter 12, Lesson 5

Kobe	electronics
Chapter 12, Lesson 5	Chapter 12, Lesson 5

hybrid car	robotics
Chapter 12, Lesson 5	Chapter 12, Lesson 5

Using New Words

Answer each question. For help, look at the lessons in the Introduction of
your textbook.

1. What are **landforms**? Which landform has a higher **elevation**, a mountain
   or a hill?

   _____

   _____

2. Where might you find the ocean, near a **Coastal Plain** or on the Interior Plains?

   _____

3. To what do **temperature** and **precipitation** refer? How do they relate to
   climate?

   _____

   _____

   _____

4. What different elements make up the **environment**?

   _____

   _____

5. What is a **natural resource**? Name two **renewable resources**.

   _____

   _____

6. What are **fuels**, and why are they **nonrenewable resources**?

   _____

   _____

7. Identify two ways we can fight **pollution**.

   _____

   _____

Using New Words

Match each term from the box with its meaning. For help, look at the
lessons in Chapter 1 of your textbook.

Dust Bowl	refinery	canyon	mesa	petrochemical
aqueduct	crude oil	aquifer	drought	dry farming
desert	butte	erosion	spring	

1. the petroleum that bubbles up from
the ground

_____

2. the slow wearing away of the land
by water, wind, or ice

_____

3. a pipe that carries water to cities
and farms

_____

4. a place where underground water
comes to the surface

_____

5. a deep, narrow valley with steep
sides

_____

6. a hill with a flat top, but smaller
than a mesa

_____

7. dry lands where little rain falls

_____

8. a way to grow crops with only a
small amount of water

_____

9. a chemical made from petroleum

_____

10. a factory where crude oil is
separated into different parts

_____

11. a hill with a flat top, smaller than a
plateau but larger than a butte

_____

12. an area of the Great Plains
devastated by droughts and dust
storms in the 1930s

_____

13. underground layers of rock or
gravel that trap water

_____

14. a period of little or no rainfall

_____

Using New Words

Answer each question to complete the activity. For help, look at the lessons in Chapter 2 of your textbook.

1. How was **adobe** important to the Hopi way of life?

   _____

   _____

2. What is cashmere and how is it important to the Mongolians?

   _____

   _____

3. How did a ranch depend upon **vaqueros**?

   _____

   _____

4. What does the Spanish word **conquistador** mean in English?

   _____

5. Why did Spanish settlers build **missions** in the Southwest?

   _____

   _____

6. What effect did the invention of **barbed wire** have on **cattle drives**?

   _____

   _____

7. What is the purpose of **NAFTA**?

   _____

   _____

8. Why did millions of Americans move to the **Sun Belt**? _____

   _____

9. Why does the Southwest attract **astronomers**?

   _____

   _____

Vocabulary Power

Activities

Using New Words

Answer the questions to complete the activity. For help, look at the lessons in Chapter 3 of your textbook.

1. Describe the difference between a river's **source** and its **mouth**.

   _____

2. Where and how does the Mississippi River create a **delta**? _____

   _____

   _____

3. What is a **river basin** and a **tributary**?

   _____

   _____

4. What keeps the **port** of New Orleans bustling?

   _____

   _____

5. How does the Southeastern **growing season** affect **agriculture** in the region?

   _____

6. Why are peanuts and rice called **cash crops**?

   _____

7. When do people become **tourists**?

   _____

8. What is **coal**? Why did it become an important **industry**?

   _____

   _____

   _____

9. Why are **labor unions** and **technology** important to coal miners?

   _____

   _____

Using New Words

Match the terms in the box with the clues below. Write the correct term on the line provided. For help, look at the lessons in Chapter 4 of your textbook.

Emancipation Proclamation	Confederacy	council	boycott
Underground Railroad	colony	abolition	segregation
Declaration of Independence	civil rights	Union	Trail of Tears
House of Burgesses	Civil War	apartheid	

1. the name given to a tragic Cherokee journey to Oklahoma

   _____

2. a group of people who helped enslaved Africans escape to freedom

   _____

3. a country formed by seceding Southern states

   _____

4. another name for the Northern states

   _____

5. a document freeing enslaved people living in the Confederate states

   _____

6. the fighting between the North and the South that lasted four years

   _____

7. a document explaining the colonial decision to be free of English rule

   _____

8. a group of people who meet to talk and make decisions

   _____

9. a place ruled by a distant country

   _____

10. a group of citizens who made laws for the colony of Virginia

   _____

11. an end to slavery

   _____

12. a refusal to buy or use a company's product or service

   _____

13. to set a group of people apart

   _____

14. the right of people to be treated equally under the law

   _____

15. a system of laws that took away the rights and freedoms of blacks in South Africa

   _____

Using New Words

Use the terms in the box to complete the puzzle . For help, look at the lessons in Chapter 5 of your textbook.

| glacier |
| broadleaf |
| harbor |
| foliage |
| fall line |
| needleleaf |
| granite |
| bay |
| urban |

Across

1. _____ is a very hard rock that is used to build buildings.

3. A huge sheet of ice slowly moving across the land is a _____.

7. The leaves of a _____ tree change color in autumn.

8. In the 1920s _____ areas became overcrowded.

9. The Appalachian plateau meets the Atlantic Coastal Plain at the _____. (2 words)

Down

2. A _____ tree is also called an evergreen.

4. People can safely dock their boats in a _____.

5. A _____ is a part of a body of water that cuts deeply into the land.

6. People come to the Northeast to see the fall _____.

Using New Words

Circle the term in each group that does not belong with the rest. Then write a sentence using the remaining words. For help, look at the lessons in Chapter 6 of your textbook.

1. sachems   commute   Iroquois Confederacy   Grand Council

_____

_____

2. Minutemen   patriots   American Revolution   megalopolis

_____

_____

3. longhouse   tenement   sweatshop   immigrant

_____

_____

4. suburb   commute   megalopolis   Boston Massacre

_____

_____

5. commute   Boswash   terrorism   urban

_____

_____

Using New Words

Choose a term from the box to match each phrase. For help, look at the lessons in Chapter 7 of your textbook.

lake effect	blizzard	taconite	open-pit mining
reclamation	tornado	prairie	ore
livestock	iron		

1. farm animals, such as cattle, pigs, and chickens

   _____

2. refers to the effect of the Great Lakes on the climate of the Midwest

   _____

3. winter storms with temperatures below 20° F, strong winds, and lots of snow

   _____

4. a flat area thickly covered with tall grass and wildflowers

   _____

5. a metal used in making steel

   _____

6. the creation of a mine by clearing the area of all plants and soil, then using explosives and giant power shovels to dig out the ore

   _____

7. a dangerous and destructive whirling funnel of wind

   _____

8. a flintlike rock that contains relatively small amounts of iron minerals

   _____

9. the practice of restoring the land after open-pit mining

   _____

10. a rock that contains a metal

    _____

Using New Words

Answer each question to complete the activity. For help, look at the lessons in Chapter 8 of your textbook.

1. What attracted a **pioneer** to the **frontier** in the 1800s?

   _____

2. Which method of transportation—a **flatboat** or **Conestoga wagon**—
   would you prefer? Why?

   _____

   _____

3. How did **mass production** help lower the cost of cars?

   _____

   _____

4. How does a **combine** help farmers?

   _____

   _____

5. What does the **food processing** industry do?

   _____

6. What is an **agribusiness**?

   _____

   _____

7. How did the **Great Migration** and the invention of **robots** affect the growth of
   industry in the Middle West?

   _____

   _____

   _____

Using New Words

Add vowels to finish the words in the grid below. Afterward, finish the chart by writing each word in the puzzle next to its definition. For help, look at the lessons in Chapter 9 of your textbook.

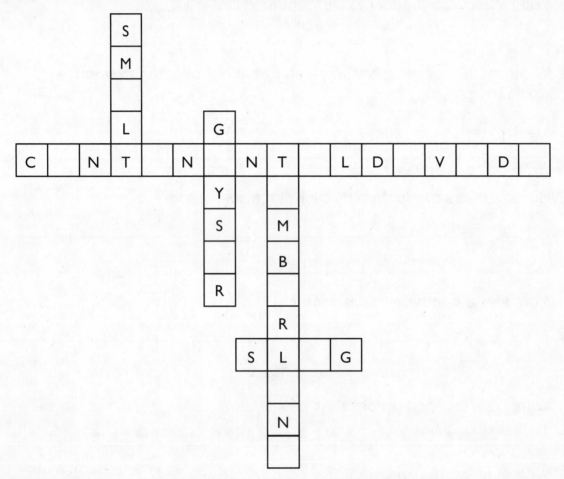

WORD	DEFINITION
	an imaginary line that runs north to south along the peaks of the Rocky Mountains
	the point above which it is too cold for trees to grow
	the process of using high temperatures to separate pure metals from rock
	a kind of hot spring that releases jets of steam and water periodically
	waste material that forms on the surface of liquid metal

Using New Words

If you need help in completing the crossword, look at the lessons in Chapter 10 of your textbook.

Down

1. a governmental division of Switzerland
2. surrounded on all sides by land
3. a journey taken for a specific purpose

Across

4. the right to vote
5. meaning *across a continent*
6. an empty town, without people
7. an agreement in writing between two or more groups
8. a narrow passage through land

Using New Words

Use the clues below and the words in the box to fill in the crossword puzzle. For help, look at the lessons in Chapter 11 of your textbook.

| deforestation | volcano | Central Valley Project |
| fertilizer | logging | rain shadow | lava |

Across

2. chemicals that make soil more fertile

4. a break in Earth's surface through which hot gases and liquid rock can erupt

5. the process by which trees are cut down and moved out of the forest

6. an irrigation system through which dams and canals bring water to dry land in California (3 words)

Down

1. the cutting down of a forest

3. a process that causes an area to stay fairly dry because rain clouds have already dropped their moisture by the time they reach it (2 words)

7. liquid rock that comes out of an erupting volcano

Vocabulary Power

Activities

Using New Words

Answer each question to complete the activity. For help, look at the lessons in Chapter 12 of your textbook.

1. What is the **electronics** industry?

_____

_____

_____

2. What is **urban sprawl**?

_____

_____

3. What was the **Gold Rush** of 1848?

_____

_____

4. What is silicon?

_____

_____

5. Who were the **forty niners**?

_____

_____

6. How is a **hybrid car** powered?

_____

_____

7. Why are **ghost towns** scattered throughout the West?

_____

_____

Name: _____ Date: _____

Using New Words

Answer each question. For help, look at the lessons in the Introduction of your textbook.

1. What are **landforms**? Which landform has a higher **elevation**, a mountain or a hill?

   the shapes that make up Earth's surface; a mountain has

   higher elevation

2. Where might you find the ocean, near a **Coastal Plain** or on the Interior Plains?

   near a Coastal Plain

3. To what do **temperature** and **precipitation** refer? How do they relate to climate?

   Temperature is a measure of the hotness or coldness of air.

   Precipitation is the moisture that falls to the ground.

   Temperature and precipitation are the two parts of climate.

4. What different elements make up the **environment**?

   The environment includes landforms and the natural

   resources of a region.

5. What is a **natural resource**? Name two **renewable resources**.

   A natural resource is a material found in nature that people

   use. Trees and water are examples of renewable resources.

6. What are **fuels**, and why are they **nonrenewable resources**?

   Fuels are sources of heat or energy. There is a limited supply

   of fuels. When we have used up a fuel, it will be gone forever.

7. Identify two ways we can fight pollution.

   We can fight pollution by reusing cans and bottles—and by

   walking or biking instead of taking a car.

©Macmillan/McGraw-Hill

Name: _____ Date: _____

Using New Words

Match each term from the box with its meaning. For help, look at the lessons in Chapter 1 of your textbook.

Dust Bowl	refinery	canyon	mesa	petrochemical
aqueduct	crude oil	aquifer	drought	dry farming
desert	butte	erosion	spring	

1. the petroleum that bubbles up from the ground

   crude oil

2. the slow wearing away of the land by water, wind, or ice

   erosion

3. a pipe that carries water to cities and farms

   aqueduct

4. a place where underground water comes to the surface

   spring

5. a deep, narrow valley with steep sides

   canyon

6. a hill with a flat top, but smaller than a mesa

   butte

7. dry lands where little rain falls

   desert

8. a way to grow crops with only a small amount of water

   dry farming

9. a chemical made from petroleum

   petrochemical

10. a factory where crude oil is separated into different parts

    refinery

11. a hill with a flat top, smaller than a plateau but larger than a butte

    mesa

12. an area of the Great Plains devastated by droughts and dust storms in the 1930s

    Dust Bowl

13. underground layers of rock or gravel that trap water

    aquifer

14. a period of little or no rainfall

    drought

©Macmillan/McGraw-Hill

Name: _____ Date: _____

Using New Words

Answer the questions to complete the activity. For help, look at the lessons in Chapter 3 of your textbook.

1. Describe the difference between a river's **source** and its **mouth**.
   A river begins at its source, and ends at its mouth.

2. Where and how does the Mississippi River create a **delta**? **The Mississippi delta lies at the river's mouth. It's the place where the river deposits soil as it flows out to sea. The soil is good for farming.**

3. What is a river **basin** and a **tributary**?
   A river basin is all the land drained by a river and its tributaries. A tributary is a body of water that flows into a river.

4. What keeps the port of New Orleans bustling?
   Ships take goods from the port at New Orleans to various places in the U.S. and around the world.

5. How does the Southeastern **growing season** affect agriculture in the region? **The long growing season enables farmers to grow many crops.**

6. Why are peanuts and rice called **cash crops**?
   They are grown to be sold for money.

7. When do people become **tourists**?
   People are tourists when they're on vacation.

8. What is **coal**? Why did it become an important **industry**? **Coal is a valuable mineral found in the earth. When coal burns it gives off energy in the form of heat. More than half of our country's electricity comes from power that burns coal.**

9. Why are **labor unions** and **technology** important to coal miners? **Both improved working conditions for coal miners.**

©Macmillan/McGraw-Hill

Name: _____ Date: _____

Using New Words

Answer each question to complete the activity. For help, look at the lessons in Chapter 2 of your textbook.

1. How was **adobe** important to the Hopi way of life?
   The Hopi built their homes from adobe bricks. These were made by mixing clay and straw together.

2. What is **cashmere** and how is it important to the Mongolians? **Cashmere is wool from goats. About one third of the world's cashmere comes from Mongolia.**

3. How did a ranch depend upon **vaqueros**?
   Vaquero is Spanish for cowboy. The vaqueros were experts on horses and herding.

4. What does the Spanish word **conquistador** mean in English? **conqueror**

5. Why did Spanish settlers build **missions** in the Southwest? **The Spanish built missions to teach Christianity and European culture to Native Americans.**

6. What effect did the invention of **barbed wire** have on cattle drives? **The invention finished cattle drives, because cowboys couldn't move cattle across land fenced-in by barbed wire.**

7. What is the purpose of **NAFTA**?
   The purpose of NAFTA is to strengthen trading ties among the three countries of North America.

8. Why did millions of Americans move to the **Sun Belt**? **Americans were attracted by new jobs, warm weather, and less crowded cities.**

9. Why does the Southwest attract **astronomers**?
   The clear, dry air of the Southwest makes it a good place for astronomers to study the planets and stars.

©Macmillan/McGraw-Hill

61

62

Using New Words

Vocabulary Power — Activities

Name: _____ Date: _____

Match the terms in the box with the clues below. Write the correct term on the line provided. For help, look at the lessons in Chapter 4 of your textbook.

Emancipation Proclamation	Confederacy	council	boycott
Underground Railroad	colony	abolition	segregation
Declaration of Independence	civil rights	Union	Trail of Tears
House of Burgesses	Civil War	apartheid	

1. the name given to a tragic Cherokee journey to Oklahoma
   Trail of Tears

2. a group of people who helped enslaved Africans escape to freedom
   Underground Railroad

3. a country formed by seceding Southern states
   Confederacy

4. another name for the Northern states
   Union

5. a document freeing enslaved people living in the Confederate states
   Emancipation Proclamation

6. the fighting between the North and the South that lasted four years
   Civil War

7. a document explaining the colonial decision to be free of English rule
   Declaration of Independence

8. a group of people who meet to talk and make decisions
   council

9. a place ruled by a distant country
   colony

10. a group of citizens who made laws for the colony of Virginia
    House of Burgesses

11. an end to slavery
    abolition

12. a refusal to buy or use a company's product or service
    boycott

13. to set a group of people apart
    segregation

14. the right of people to be treated equally under the law
    civil rights

15. a system of laws that took away the rights and freedoms of blacks in South Africa
    apartheid

Unit 2 · Chapter 4   Use with pages 138–176.   **51**

©Macmillan/McGraw-Hill

Using New Words

Vocabulary Power — Activities

Name: _____ Date: _____

Use the terms in the box to complete the puzzle . For help, look at the lessons in Chapter 5 of your textbook.

glacier	broadleaf	harbor
foliage	fall line	needleleaf
granite	bay	urban

(Crossword grid answers: GRANITE, GLACIER, BROADLEAF, URBAN, FALL LINE, FOLIAGE, HARBOR, BAY)

Across

1. _____ is a very hard rock that is used to build buildings.

3. A huge sheet of ice slowly moving across the land is a _____.

7. The leaves of a _____ tree change color in autumn.

8. In the 1920s _____ areas became overcrowded.

9. The Appalachian plateau meets the Atlantic Coastal Plain at the _____. (2 words)

Down

2. A _____ tree is also called an evergreen.

4. People can safely dock their boats in a _____.

5. A _____ is a part of a body of water that cuts deeply into the land.

6. People come to the Northeast to see the fall _____.

52   Use with pages 178–203.   Unit 3 · Chapter 5

©Macmillan/McGraw-Hill

Name: ______________________ Date: __________

Vocabulary Power

Activities

Using New Words

Circle the term in each group that does not belong with the rest. Then write a sentence using the remaining words. For help, look at the lessons in Chapter 6 of your textbook.

1. sachems (commute) Iroquois Confederacy Grand Council
   Possible answer: The Iroquois Confederacy was ruled by a Grand Council of 50 sachems.

2. Minutemen patriots American Revolution (megalopolis)
   Possible answer: The Minutemen were patriots who fought in the American Revolution.

3. (longhouse) tenement sweatshop immigrant
   Possible answer: Many immigrants in the late 1800s lived in tenements and worked in sweatshops.

4. suburb commute megalopolis (Boston Massacre)
   Possible answer: Many people who live in the megalopolis of the Northeast commute to work from the suburbs.

5. commute Boswash (terrorism) urban
   In the Boswash area, people can commute quickly from one urban center to another.

©Macmillan/McGraw-Hill

Name: ______________________ Date: __________

Vocabulary Power

Activities

Using New Words

Choose a term from the box to match each phrase. For help, look at the lessons in Chapter 7 of your textbook.

lake effect	blizzard	taconite	open-pit mining
reclamation	tornado	prairie	ore
livestock	iron		

1. farm animals, such as cattle, pigs, and chickens **livestock**
2. refers to the effect of the Great Lakes on the climate of the Midwest **lake effect**
3. winter storms with temperatures below 20° F, strong winds, and lots of snow **blizzard**
4. a flat area thickly covered with tall grass and wildflowers **prairie**
5. a metal used in making steel **iron**
6. the creation of a mine by clearing the area of all plants and soil, then using explosives and giant power shovels to dig out the ore **open-pit mining**
7. a dangerous and destructive whirling funnel of wind **tornado**
8. a flintlike rock that contains relatively small amounts of iron minerals **taconite**
9. the practice of restoring the land after open-pit mining **reclamation**
10. a rock that contains a metal **ore**

©Macmillan/McGraw-Hill

Name: _____   Date: _____

Using New Words

Answer each question to complete the activity. For help, look at the lessons in Chapter 8 of your textbook.

1. What attracted a **pioneer** to the **frontier** in the 1800s?

inexpensive land and dreams of a better life

2. Which method of transportation—a **flatboat** or **Conestoga wagon**—would you prefer? Why?

Possible answer: I would prefer traveling over land in a

Conestoga wagon. I can't swim and feel safer on land.

3. How did **mass production** help lower the cost of cars?

In mass production, cars are made on an assembly line. The new

way of producing cars was faster and cheaper than the old way.

4. How does a **combine** help farmers?

A combine cuts and threshes wheat, removing the grain from

the stalk.

5. What does the **food processing** industry do?

It uses raw food to create products to be sold to consumers.

6. What is an **agribusiness**?

An agribusiness combines farming with other businesses,

such as food processing.

7. How did the **Great Migration** and the invention of **robots** affect the growth of industry in the Middle West?

The Great Migration brought thousands of African American

workers to the region; robots brought the high-tech industry.

©Macmillan/McGraw-Hill

Name: _____   Date: _____

Using New Words

Add vowels to finish the words in the grid below. Afterward, finish the chart by writing each word in the puzzle next to its definition. For help, look at the lessons in Chapter 9 of your textbook.

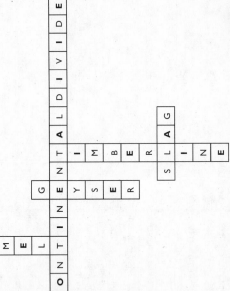

WORD	DEFINITION
Continental Divide	an imaginary line that runs north to south along the peaks of the Rocky Mountains
timberline	the point above which it is too cold for trees to grow
smelt	the process of using high temperatures to separate pure metals from rock
geyser	a kind of hot spring that releases jets of steam and water periodically
slag	waste material that forms on the surface of liquid metal

©Macmillan/McGraw-Hill

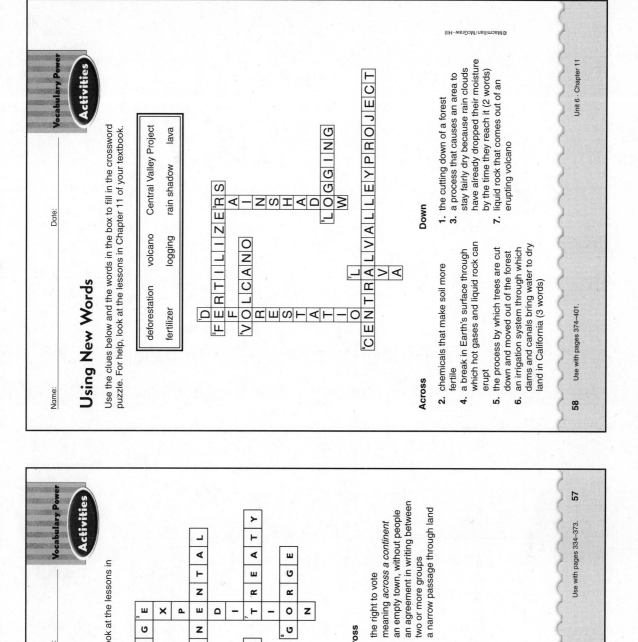

Using New Words

If you need help in completing the crossword, look at the lessons in Chapter 10 of your textbook.

Down

1. a governmental division of Switzerland
2. surrounded on all sides by land
3. a journey taken for a specific purpose

Across

4. the right to vote
5. meaning *across a continent*
6. an empty town, without people
7. an agreement in writing between two or more groups
8. a narrow passage through land

Using New Words

Use the clues below and the words in the box to fill in the crossword puzzle. For help, look at the lessons in Chapter 11 of your textbook.

deforestation	volcano	Central Valley Project
fertilizer	logging	rain shadow lava

Across

2. chemicals that make soil more fertile
4. a break in Earth's surface through which hot gases and liquid rock can erupt
5. the process by which trees are cut down and moved out of the forest
6. an irrigation system through which dams and canals bring water to dry land in California (3 words)

Down

1. the cutting down of a forest
3. a process that causes an area to stay fairly dry because rain clouds have already dropped their moisture by the time they reach it (2 words)
7. liquid rock that comes out of an erupting volcano

Name: _____ Date: _____

Using New Words

Answer each question to complete the activity. For help, look at the
lessons in Chapter 12 of your textbook.

1. What is the electronics industry?

   An industry that creates high-technology products, such as

   televisions.

2. What is urban sprawl?

   Urban sprawl is the uncontrolled spread of buildings around

   a city.

3. What was the Gold Rush of 1848?

   The Gold Rush was a sudden movement of people to the part

   of California where gold had been found.

4. What is silicon?

   Silicon is an element found in Earth's crust and used in

   making electronic products.

5. Who were the forty niners?

   They were gold-seekers who rushed to California in 1849,

   during the Gold Rush.

6. How is a hybrid car powered?

   A hybrid car combines a battery-powered motor with a gas

   engine.

7. Why are ghost towns scattered throughout the West?

   These towns were deserted after the gold rush. They are

   now tourist attractions.

         Use with pages 402–441.

Word Association Chart

	Related Words and Phrases	
Vocabulary	**Before Reading**	**After Reading**

Word Sort Chart

Category: _____

Words

Word Links Chart

Word	Links to: _____